Selections From
SPANISH POETRY

Illustrated by Anne Marie Jauss

HARVEY HOUSE, INC.,
Irvington-on-Hudson, N. Y.

Selections
From
SPANISH
POETRY

by SEYMOUR RESNICK

Harvey House, Inc.
Publishers
Irvington-on-Hudson, New York

Acknowledgements

"King Don Sancho," translated by Nicholson B. Adams in THE HERITAGE
OF SPAIN by Nicholson B. Adams. © 1959 by Holt, Rinehart and Winston,
Inc. Reprinted by permission of Holt, Rinehart and Winston, Inc., N. Y.

"Three Moorish Girls," translated by Jean Rogers Longland; "Grace and
Beauty Has the Maid" and "Pirate's Song," both translated by Alice Jane McVan.
Reprinted courtesy of The Hispanic Society of America, N. Y. from TRANS-
LATIONS FROM HISPANIC POETS.

"Death Warnings"—"Sonnet from the Spanish of Don Francisco de Quevedo."
Reprinted with permission of The Macmillan Company from POEMS by
John Masefield. © 1912 by The Macmillan Company. © 1940 by John
Masefield.

"Rider's Song," translated by Eleanor L. Turnbull in CONTEMPORARY
SPANISH POETRY. Reprinted by permission of Eleanor L. Turnbull and
The John Hopkins Press, Maryland.

Contents

*LITERAL PROSE TRANSLATION BY THE EDITOR

*LITERAL PROSE TRANSLATION BY THE EDITOR

Foreword

Present-day methods of teaching Spanish are strongly influenced by the realization of the creative power of speech. We have finally come to understand that language is not merely an assembly of grammar rules or an accumulation of vocabulary, although both are inseparably connected with language. The human voice with its articulated sounds lends new strength to our ideas, for they take on intonation and rhythm which condition the effect of our speech upon the hearer. In the spoken word with its potentiality to generate a whole atmosphere, language instructors should find a most effective teaching resource. Human speech, in my opinion, is one of the world's greatest marvels, a gift which gives man one of his most obvious and important superiorities over animals. Speech involves much more than lip movement; in speech subtle vibrations produced by man's voice convey an intangible something which goes beyond the expression of the written or printed word. The publication of this volume of poetry selections is accordingly most timely, since it provides an excellent basis for oral practice in Spanish.

In order to benefit fully from Dr. Resnick's anthology, the reader must recite the selections aloud. The English translations are helpful, of course, as they make the verses immediately comprehensible and minimize the obstacles presented by unfamiliar and archaic vocabulary. Yet even the good translations provided here cannot impart the same meaning as the original words used by the Spanish poets, since these words call for special sounds and evoke special connotations in Spanish.

Let us take two examples to show how this book offers access to the world contained in Spanish words. First we shall consider the excerpt from Jorge Manrique's immortal *coplas*. As the reader recites aloud the first three lines of the second stanza quoted by Dr. Resnick *(Nuestras vidas son los ríos/que van a dar en la mar,/que es el morir),* a forceful picture of life advancing toward its limit in this world and the mysterious frontier of the hereafter is created through two magnificent metaphors: *vidas-ríos; mar-morir.* Note how the rhythm of the verses reinforces the metaphors, emphasizing the steady flow of life and time. For the second illustration I wish to call your attention to Quevedo and his famous satire on the powers of money. The two-line refrain, *Poderoso caballero/es don Dinero,* is sufficient to tear Sir Money to pieces. Notice the five *o*'s used here. As we pronounce the Spanish *o* by rounding the lips and expelling the air forcefully, Quevedo's sentence acquires special irony of expression through the explosive, pompously inflated sounds which describe Sir Money.

In preparing this volume Dr. Seymour Resnick, a seasoned and competent language teacher, has rendered a significant service to both teaching colleagues and Spanish students. Through his anthology the student may become familiarized, early in his work, with certain facts and useful information about the literature of Spain. Thus his selections prepare the ground for further readings, besides directing the pupil's attention to some of the literary treasures that constitute the foundation of Spanish.

MANUEL SALAS
Douglass College,
Rutgers University

July, 1962

Preface

Selections from Spanish Poetry was compiled for use as a supplementary text in regular Spanish classes at the junior high school level and above. This collection of Spanish poetry has several pedagogical aims:

1. Reading and recitation of poetry is an aid in developing good pronunciation. Most of the selections are short enough for easy memorization. It should be noted that most Spaniards and Spanish Americans are fond of reciting poetry. Many of the selections chosen here are known by heart by most educated native speakers of Spanish and by teachers of Spanish.

2. Learning of vocabulary and grammatical constructions are facilitated by English translations on opposite pages. Translations have been provided on facing pages to allow the reader to enjoy the beauty of the poems without the problem of translating. Twenty-three of the poems have literal prose translations that were prepared by the editor and arranged to match the corresponding lines of the Spanish poem. The remaining fifteen selections have verse translations, including several by Henry Wadsworth Longfellow and one by John Masefield. While the verse translations often do not match the original line for line, there is an aesthetic advantage in having some of the selections represented by poetic equivalents.

3. This volume may serve as a brief introduction to the very rich field of Spanish poetry. The selections chosen are popular favorites among native speakers of Spanish and American teachers of Spanish. Representative selections have been chosen from the earliest Spanish poetry, beginning with the *Poem of the Cid,*

in the twelfth century, through the medieval and renaissance periods, the Golden Age (ca. 1550-1650), the eighteenth and nineteenth centuries. Since our main criterion for choosing the poems has been that they be popular favorites that have stood up under the test of time, we have included only one poem of the twentieth century, García Lorca's *Canción de jinete* (Rider's Song), which seems to have already achieved the status of a modern classic.

The present volume includes only poetry of Spain and not that of Spanish America, which merits a treatment of its own.

For those who prefer to read the selections in order of difficulty rather than in chronological order, the following groupings may serve as a guide:

Simple
Don't Look at Me
On Sunday I Saw Her at Mass
Grace and Beauty Has the Maid
Let Nothing Disturb Thee
Life of Retirement
On Leaving Prison
Poem
The Loveliest Girl
What Is Life?
Arabesque
In This Treacherous World
Rima XXI

Average
"Welcome Death"
The Prisoner

The editor wishes to thank his friend and colleague Marion E. Tupper for many useful suggestions.

S. R.

Poem of the Cid

The bearded one (the Cid) bent down
and picked up his daughters in his arms,
he pressed them against his heart, for he loved them very much.
The tears rolled down from his eyes, he was sighing so deeply:
"Alas, Doña Ximena, my dearest wife,
I have loved you as my own soul,
but now you see that we must part while we both live;
I must go and you must stay behind."

The great epic of early Spanish literature, the Poem of the Cid, *was written by an anonymous poet around the year 1140, some forty years after the death of Rodrigo Díaz de Bivar, Spain's national hero. The poem contains a realistic and human portrayal of the hero. This is part of the moving scene toward the beginning of the poem, when the Cid, banished from Castile by King Alfonso VI, takes leave of his wife and two young daughters.*

Enclinó las manos la barba vellida,
a las sues fijas en brazos las prendía,
llególas al corazón, ca mucho las quería.
Llora de los ojos, tan fuertemientre sospira:
—Ya, doña Jimena, la mi mugier tan complida,
como a la mie alma yo tanto vos quería;
ya lo veedes que partir nos hemos en vida:
yo iré, y vos fincaredes remanida.

ANONYMOUS

Praise of little women

I wish to make my sermon brief — to shorten my oration —
For a never-ending sermon is my utter detestation:
I like short women, suits at law without procrastination,
And am always most delighted with things of short duration.

A babbler is a laughing-stock; he's a fool who's always grinning;
But little women love so much, one falls in love with sinning.
There are women who are very tall, and yet not worth the
  winning,
And in the change of short for long repentance finds beginning.

In a little precious stone what splendor meets the eyes!
In a little lump of sugar how much of sweetness lies!
So in a little woman love grows and multiplies;
You recollect the proverb says, — "a word unto the Wise."

And as within the little rose you find the richest dyes,
And in the little grain of gold much price and value lies,
As from a little balsam much odor doth arise,
So in a little woman there's a taste of paradise.

There's naught can be compared to her, throughout the wide
  creation;
She is a paradise on earth — our greatest consolation —
So cheerful, gay and happy, so free from all vexation;
In fine, she's better in the proof than in anticipation.

De las propiedades que las dueñas chicas han

Quiero abreviaros, señores, la mi predicación,
ca siempre me pagué de pequeño sermón
y de dueña pequeña y de breve razón:
ca lo poco y bien dicho finca en el corazón.

Del que mucho fabla ríen, quien mucho ríe es loco.
Tiene la dueña chica amor grande, y non de poco:
dueñas di grandes por chicas; por grandes, chicas non troco;
mas las chicas por las grandes, non se arrepiente del troco.

En pequeña girgonza yace gran resplandor,
en azúcar muy poco yace mucho dulzor,
en la dueña pequeña yace muy gran amor:
pocas palabras cumplen al buen entendedor.

Como en chica rosa está mucha color,
en oro muy poco gran precio y gran valor,
como en poco bálsamo yace gran buen olor,
así en chica dueña yace muy gran amor.

De la mujer pequeña non hay comparación,
terrenal paraíso es, y consolación,
solaz y alegría, placer y bendición:
mejor es en la prueba que en la salutación.

If as her size increases are woman's charms decreased,
Then surely it is good to be from all the great released.
Now of two evils choose the less — said a wise man of the East,
By consequence, of woman-kind be sure to choose the least.

Translated by H. W. LONGFELLOW

Juan Ruiz, Archpriest of Hita (1283?-1350?), is the author of the humorous, satirical Libro de buen amor, *one of the greatest master-pieces of Spanish literature. The work consists of more than seven thousand verses, which vary greatly both in metrical form and in subject matter. Henry Wadsworth Longfellow translated several passages of* The Book of Good Love, *including this popular one.*

Siempre quis' mujer chica más que grande nin mayor:
non es desaguisado de gran mal ser huidor;
del mal, tomar lo menos, — dícelo el sabidor:
por ende, de las mujeres la menor es mejor.

JUAN RUIZ, ARCHPRIEST OF HITA

Mountain Song of La Finojosa

So beautiful a lass
I never saw along the border
as a cowgirl
of La Finojosa.
    As I was making my way
from Calatraveño
to Santa María,
overcome by sleep
and through rough terrain,
I lost my way
there where I saw the cowgirl
of La Finojosa.
    In a green meadow
of roses and flowers
tending her cattle
with other cow-herders,
I saw her, so charming
that I could scarcely believe
that she was a cowgirl
of La Finojosa.
    I would not have thought the roses
of spring
so beautiful,
so lovely;
to tell the truth,
had I first seen
that cowgirl
of La Finojosa.

Serranilla de la Finojosa

Moza tan hermosa
no vi en la frontera
como una vaquera
de la Finojosa.

Haciendo la vía
del Calatraveño
a Santa María,
vencido del sueño,
por tierra fragosa
perdí la carrera,
do vi la vaquera
de la Finojosa.

En un verde prado
de rosas y flores
guardando ganado
con otros pastores,
la vi tan graciosa
que apenas creyera
que fuese vaquera
de la Finojosa.

No creo las rosas
de la primavera
sean tan hermosas
ni de tal manera,
hablando sin glosa,
si antes supiera
de aquella vaquera
de la Finojosa.

I did not gaze too long
at her great beauty
lest I lose
my freedom.
But I said: "My pretty maid"
— to find out who she was —
"are you the cowgirl
of La Finojosa?"
 Laughingly
she said, "I bid you welcome,
and I understand very well
why you ask.
But she does not wish
to be courted —
this cowgirl
of La Finojosa."

The greatest literary fame of the fifteenth-century nobleman, the Marquis of Santillana (1398-1458), stems from his delightful serranillas *(mountain songs)*. The Serranilla de la Finojosa *is the most popular poem of this genre.*

No tanto mirara
su mucha beldad,
porque me dejara
en mi libertad.
Mas dije: "Donosa
(por saber quién era)
¿aquella vaquera
de la Finojosa?"
Bien como riendo
dijo: "Bien vengades,
que ya bien entiendo
lo que demandades.
No es deseosa
de amar, ni lo espera,
aquella vaquera
de la Finojosa."

MARQUIS DE SANTILLANA

Ode on the Death of His Father

Oh, let the soul her slumbers break!
Let thought be quickened and awake—
　　Awake to see
How soon this life is past and gone,
And death comes softly stealing on,
　　How silently!
Swiftly our pleasures glide away:
Our hearts recall the distant day
　　With many sighs:
The moments that are speeding fast
We heed not; but the past—the past—
　　More highly prize.

Our lives are rivers, gliding free
To that unfathomed, boundless sea,
　　The silent grave:
Thither all earthly pomp and boast
Roll, to be swallowed up and lost
　　In one dark wave.
Thither the mighty torrents stray,
Thither the brook pursues its way,
　　And tinkling rill.
There all are equal. Side by side,
The poor man and the son of pride
　　Lie calm and still.

Translated by H. W. Longfellow

Coplas por la muerte de su padre

Recuerde el alma dormida,
avive el seso y despierte
contemplando
cómo se pasa la vida,
cómo se viene la muerte
tan callando;
cuán presto se va el placer,
cómo después de acordado
da dolor,
cómo a nuestro parecer
cualquiera tiempo pasado
fué mejor.

Nuestras vidas son los ríos
que van a dar en la mar,
que es el morir;
allí van los señoríos
derechos a se acabar
y consumir;
allí los ríos caudales,
allí los otros medianos
y más chicos;
allegados, son iguales
los que viven por sus manos
y los ricos.

JORGE MANRIQUE

*The most beautiful elegy in the Spanish language is Jorge Man-
rique's (1440-1479) lament,* Coplas por la muerte de su padre, *on
the death of his father. In rich, yet simple language, reminiscent
of the finest lyrical passages in the Bible, the poet reflects upon the
transitory nature of life. The entire forty stanzas were skilfully
translated by Henry Wadsworth Longfellow. The first and third
stanzas, given here, are particularly esteemed.*

Welcome, Death

Come, gentle death! Come silently,
    And sound no knell, no warning give,
Lest the sweet bliss of welcoming thee
    Should rouse my wearied soul to live.

Come like the rapid lightning's ray,
    That wounds, but while it wounds is still;
It passes, voiceless, on its way,
    And flings its mortal barb at will.
Thus soft, thus calm, thy coming be,
    Else, death! This warning now I give,
That the sweet bliss of welcoming thee
    Will rouse my weary soul to live.

Translated by JOHN BOWRING

The Comendador Juan Escrivá (ca. 1490), author of this popular little poem, expressed a longing for death—which represented true life to many Spanish mystic poets. The opening quatrain of Ven, muerte, tan escondida, has been quoted by Cervantes, Lope de Vega, Calderón de la Barca, and others.

Ven, muerte

Ven, muerte, tan escondida,
que no te sienta conmigo,
porque el gozo de contigo
no me torne a dar la vida.

Ven como rayo que hiere,
que hasta que ha herido
no se siente su ruido,
por mejor herir do quiere:
así sea tu venida,
si no, desde aquí me obligo
que el gozo que habré contigo
me dará de nuevo vida.

JUAN ESCRIVÁ

The Prisoner

It was in the month of May,
When the warm weather comes,
When the lark sings
And the nightingale replies,
When lovers go to serve their loves;
All but I, who sad and wretched
Lie in this prison,
And do not know when it is day
Or when night comes,
Were it not for a little bird
That used to sing to me at dawn;
A hunter killed it.
May God punish him!

Of especial renown in Spanish literature is the collection of popular ballads—romances—short poems dealing with a variety of themes—love, adventure, history. Some romances are probably as old as the early epics, while others may have been composed as late as the fifteenth century. Since they were transmitted orally for many years, most of them exist in more than one version.

Of the several versions of this touching ballad about a prisoner, the short version given here is probably the most poetic and dramatic.

El prisionero

Por el mes era de mayo
cuando hace la calor,
cuando canta la calandria
y responde el ruiseñor,
cuando los enamorados
van a servir al amor,
sino yo triste, cuitado,
que vivo en esta prisión,
que ni sé cuando es de día,
ni cuando las noches son,
sino por una avecilla
que me cantaba al albor;
matómela un ballestero:
¡déle Dios mal galardón!

ANONYMOUS

Count Arnaldos

Oh, who could have such good fortune,
By the waters of the sea,
As Count Arnaldos had
On the morning of St. John!
With a hunting falcon on his hand
He was going out to hunt
When he saw a galley
Approaching land.
Its sails were made of silk
And its rigging out of lace,
And the captain who commanded it
Was singing a song
Which made the sea calm
And the winds gentle;
It made the fish that live in the deep water
Come up to the surface,
And it made the birds that fly
Come to rest on the mast.
Then spoke Count Arnaldos,
— you shall hear what he said:
"For the sake of God, oh Captain,
Teach me now your song!"
The captain answered,
He gave him this reply:
"I do not teach this song,
Except to those who with me go."

One of the most beautiful of all Spanish ballads is this enigmatic poem about the haunting, mystical song heard by Count Arnaldos.

El conde Arnaldos

¡Quién hubiese tal ventura
sobre las aguas del mar,
como hubo el conde Arnaldos
la mañana de San Juan!
Con un halcón en la mano
la caza iba a cazar;
vió venir una galera
que a tierra quiere llegar.
Las velas traía de seda,
la ejercias de un cendal;
marinero que la manda
diciendo viene un cantar
que la mar ponía en calma,
los vientos hace amainar,
los peces que andan 'nel hondo
arriba los hace andar,
las aves que andan volando
'nel mástil vienen posar.
Allí habló el conde Arnaldos,
bien oiréis lo que dirá:
—Por Dios te ruego, marinero,
dígasme ora ese cantar.
Respondióle el marinero,
tal respuesta le fué a dar:
— Yo no digo esta canción
sino a quien conmigo va.

Anonymous

King Don Sancho

King don Sancho, King don Sancho,
I warn thee, warn thee well,
That from Zamora's city
Hath come a traitor fell.
His name Vellido Dolfos,
Dolfos Vellido's son.
Ere now he wrought four treasons,
With this five will be done.
If traitor was the father,
The son is traitor more.
In don Sancho's camp they're crying
Don Sancho's wounded sore.
Vellido Dolfos killed him,
Great treason hath he done.
And after this foul murder
Through a postern gate he's run.
And through the streets of Zamora
He shouted as he stepped:
It was high time, Urraca,
That promises be kept.

Translated by NICHOLSON B. ADAMS

Many of the ancient ballads deal with historical events. This one has as its source the civil war in the eleventh century. King Sancho II of Castile was laying siege to the city of Zamora, held by his sister Doña Urraca.

Rey don Sancho

Rey don Sancho, Rey don Sancho,
no digas que no te aviso,
que de dentro de Zamora
un alevoso ha salido.
Vellido Dolfos se llama,
hijo de Dolfos Vellido;
cuatro traiciones ha hecho,
y con ésta serán cinco.
Si grande traidor fué el padre,
mayor traidor es el hijo.
Gritos dan en el real,
a don Sancho han mal herido:
muerto le ha Vellido Dolfos,
gran traición ha cometido.
Desque le tuviera muerto,
metióse por un postigo;
por las calles de Zamora
va dando voces y gritos:
— Tiempo era, Doña Urraca,
de cumplir lo prometido.

ANONYMOUS

Three Moorish Girls

Three Moorish girls I loved
In Jaen,
Axa and Fatima and Marien.

Three Moorish girls so gay
Went olive-plucking there,
And found them plucked away
In Jaen,
Axa and Fatima and Marien.

And found them plucked away
And turned back in dismay,
And pale and sad were they
In Jaen,
Axa and Fatima and Marien.

Three Moorish girls so fair,
Three Moorish girls so fair,
Went apple-plucking there
In Jaen,
Axa and Fatima and Marien.

Translated by JEAN ROGERS LONGLAND

Spanish literature abounds in such light verse as this popular folksong, which dates back to the days when the Moors were in Spain. The poem is notable for its simplicity and lyric charm.

Tres morillas

Tres morillas me enamoran
en Jaén,
Axa y Fátima y Marién.

Tres morillas tan garridas
iban a coger olivas,
y hallábanlas cogidas
en Jaén,
Axa y Fátima y Marién.

Y hallábanlas cogidas,
y tornaban desmaídas
y las colores perdidas,
en Jaén,
Axa y Fátima y Marién.

Tres moricas tan lozanas,
tres moricas tan lozanas,
iban a coger manzanas
a Jaén,
Axa y Fátima y Marién.

ANONYMOUS

Do Not Look at Me

Do not look at me, for they will see
That we are looking at one another,
And they will see in your eyes
That we love one another.
Let us not look at one another,
For when they are not looking at us,
We shall look at one another.

Another example of popular light verse is this fifteenth century poem of seven lines (seguidilla), with a modern ring. The young lovers want to look at one another but do not want everyone to read their feelings. The author plays with the verb mirar *(to look at), using it six times.*

No me mires

No me mires, que miran
que nos miramos,
y verán en tus ojos
que nos amamos.
No nos miremos,
que cuando no nos miren
nos miraremos.

ANONYMOUS

On Sunday I Saw Her at Mass

On Sunday I saw her at mass,
On Monday I smiled at her,
On Tuesday they introduced me,
On Wednesday I went to her house,
On Thursday I proposed,
On Friday I gave her the ring,
And on Saturday I was married.

This popular folk poem recounts a rapid courtship.

El domingo la vi en misa

El domingo la vi en misa,
el lunes le sonreí,
el martes me presentaron,
el miércoles fuí a su casa,
el jueves me declaré,
el viernes le di el anillo,
y el sábado me casé.

ANONYMOUS

They Tell Me to Get Married

They tell me to get married —
But I don't want a husband, no!

I would rather live secure
In these mountains without care,
Than have doubts about
Whether I shall be happy in marriage or not.
They tell me to get married —
But I don't want a husband, no!

Mother, I shall not marry,
So as not to have a dull life,
And perhaps waste
The gifts that God has given me.
They tell me to get married —
But I don't want a husband, no!

Such a man will not be born,
Nor has he been, who is to be my husband;
And since I know
That I am the flower of the girls,
They tell me to get married —
But I don't want a husband, no!

Gil Vicente (1470?-1539?), one of Portugal's greatest poets and dramatists, wrote a number of his plays in Spanish. He also often introduced Spanish lyrics in his Portuguese plays. In his play Auto de la Sibila Casandra, *the heroine Casandra gives this spirited answer to the suggestion that she marry.*

Dicen que me case yo

Dicen que me case yo;
no quiero marido, no.

Más quiero vivir segura
nesta sierra a mi soltura,
que no estar en ventura
si casaré bien o no.
Dicen que me case yo;
no quiero marido, no.

Madre, no seré casada,
por no ver vida cansada,
o quizá mal empleada
la gracia que Dios me dió.
Dicen que me case yo;
no quiero marido, no.

No será ni es nacido
tal para ser mi marido;
y pues que tengo sabido
que la flor me la só,
dicen que me case yo;
no quiero marido, no.

GIL VICENTE

Grace and Beauty Has the Maid

Grace and beauty has the maid;
Could anything more lovely be?

Sailor, you who live on ships,
Did you ever see
Any ship or sail or star
As beautiful as she?

Knight of war, in armor clad,
Did you ever see
Horse or arms or battlefield
As beautiful as she?

Shepherd, you who guard your flock,
Did you ever see
Cattle, vale, or mountain range
As beautiful as she?

Translated by ALICE JANE McVAN

At the end of Auto de la Sibila Casandra *the poem above is addressed to the Virgin Mary. It is considered one of the most beautiful lyrics in all Spanish literature.*

Muy graciosa es la doncella

Muy graciosa es la doncella,
¡cómo es bella y hermosa!

Digas tú, el marinero,
que en las naves vivías,
si la nave o la vela
o la estrella es tan bella.

Digas tú, el caballero,
que las armas vestías,
si el caballo o las armas
o la guerra es tan bella.

Digas tú, el pastorcico,
que el ganadico guardas,
si el ganado o los valles o la sierra
es tan bella.

GIL VICENTE

Sonnet X

O precious locket, found by luckless me,
Precious and pleasing when the Lord hath willed;
You are made one with my own memory,
And with my death you too shall be stilled.

Who could foresee in the so recent past
When you were a source of true joy to me,
That our delightful bliss would not long last,
But would turn to heartache and misery?

For in one sole hour you did remove
All the joy and good you did ever bring;
Take, too, the grief left by you with me.

If not, I shall think you did falsely love,
And did leave me a victim to Remorse's sting
That I might die with your sad memory.

Garcilaso de la Vega (1503?-1536), courtier and soldier, was the finest Spanish poet of the early sixteenth century—especially known for his development of the sonnet. Sonnet X is a notable example of his work. The poet has learned of the death of Isabel Freire, the lady of his dreams, and he addresses his grief to a keepsake (perhaps a lock of her hair).

Soneto X

¡Oh dulces prendas, por mi mal halladas,
dulces y alegres cuando Dios quería!
Juntas estáis en la memoria mía,
y con ella en mi muerte conjuradas.

¿Quién me dijera, cuando en las pasadas
horas en tanto bien por vos me veía,
que me habíades de ser en algún día
con tan grave dolor representadas?

Pues en una hora junto me llevastes
todo el bien que por términos me distes,
llevadme junto el mal que me dejastes.

Si no, sospecharé que me pusistes
en tantos bienes, porque deseastes
verme morir entre memorias tristes.

GARCILASO DE LA VEGA

Madrigal

Eyes clear and serene,
If you know you are praised for a sweet glance,
Why, when you look at me, do you look angry?
When your gaze is most compassionate
You appear most beautiful to the one who is looking at you,
Do not look at me with anger,
Lest you appear less beautiful.
Oh, maddening torment!
Eyes clear and serene,
Even though you look at me like that, look at me!

Madrigal

Ojos claros, serenos,
si de un dulce mirar sois alabados,
¿por qué, si me miráis, miráis airados?
Si cuanto más piadosos,
más bellos parecéis a aquel que os mira,
no me miréis con ira,
porque no parezcáis menos hermosos.
¡Ay tormentos rabiosos!
Ojos claros, serenos,
ya que así me miráis, miradme al menos.

GUTIERRE DE CETINA

This madrigal by Gutierre de Cetina (1520?-1560?) is one of the most popular poems of love in the Spanish language.

Let Nothing Disturb Thee

Let nothing disturb thee,
Nothing affright thee,
All things are passing,
God never changeth;
Patient endurance
Attaineth to all things;
Whom God possesseth
In nothing is wanting:
Alone God sufficeth.

Translated by H. W. LONGFELLOW

Santa Teresa (1515-1582) was one of Spain's great mystic authors in both prose and verse. Let Nothing Disturb Thee *was found in her breviary after her death; it is often called Saint Teresa's bookmark. It is remarkable for its brevity, simplicity, and implicit faith.*

Nada te turbe

Nada te turbe,
nada te espante,
todo se pasa,
Dios no se muda;
la paciencia
todo lo alcanza;
quien a Dios tiene
nada le falta:
solo Dios basta.

SANTA TERESA

Life of Retirement

What a restful life
Is that of the one who flees the noise of the world,
And follows the hidden
Path along which have gone
The few wise men who have been in this world!

Fray Luis de León (1527-1591), an Augustinian professor of the University of Salamanca, is considered Spain's greatest poet by many critics. His polished classic odes express his yearnings for peace of mind and spirit. This is the opening stanza of his Vida retirada, *also called* La vida del campo (Country Life).

Vida retirada

¡Qué descansada vida
la del que huye el mundanal ruido,
y sigue la escondida
senda por donde han ido
los pocos sabios que en el mundo han sido!

FRAY LUIS DE LEÓN

On Leaving Prison

Here, envy and falsehood
Kept me imprisoned;
Blessed is the humble state
Of the scholar who withdraws
From this wicked world;
And with simple house and food
In the delightful countryside,
Communes with God alone,
And spends his life alone,
Neither envied nor envious.

Fray Luis de León was imprisoned by the Inquisition for almost five years, and upon his return to the University of Salamanca he is said to have begun his first lecture with the following words: "As we were saying yesterday . . ."

Al salir de la cárcel

Aquí la envidia y mentira
me tuvieron encerrado;
dichoso el humilde estado
del sabio que se retira
de aqueste mundo malvado;
y con pobre mesa y casa
en el campo deleitoso,
con sólo Dios se compasa
y a solas la vida pasa
ni envidiado ni envidioso.

FRAY LUIS DE LEÓN

Poem

Help me! The waves are carrying me away!
Help me! The sea is carrying me away!
Help me! I am allowing myself to be carried off
Without order and without thought
And I am going farther away from heaven,
Which I cannot reach.
Help me! The waves are carrying me away!
Help me! The sea is carrying me away!

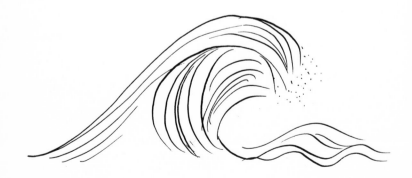

Canción

¡Hola! que me lleva la ola.
¡Hola! que me lleva la mar.
　¡Hola! que llevarme dejo
sin orden y sin consejo,
y que del cielo me alejo,
donde no puedo llegar.
¡Hola! que me lleva la ola.
¡Hola! que me lleva la mar.

LOPE DE VEGA

The prolific Lope de Vega (1562-1635) wrote some 1800 plays (all in verse), several prose works, and innumerable lyric poems. This brief example of his writing, as simple as a folksong, lends itself easily to mystical interpretation.

The Loveliest Girl

The loveliest girl
Of our town
Today a widow and alone,
And only yesterday about to be married,
Seeing that her beloved
Is going off to war,
Says to her mother,
Who is listening to her grief:
"Let me weep
By the shores of the sea."

La más bella niña

La más bella niña
de nuestro lugar,
hoy viuda y sola
y ayer por casar,
viendo que sus ojos
a la guerra van,
a su madre dice
que escucha su mal:
Dejadme llorar
orillas del mar.

LUIS DE GÓNGORA

Luis de Góngora (1561-1627), in an attempt to refine his poetry, developed an obscure style which has made him one of the most controversial figures in Spanish literature. He also wrote many charming lyrics in a traditional, popular vein—like this one, in which a young bride laments the departure of her husband to fight in the wars. This is the first of six stanzas.

Let Me Go Warm

Let me go warm and merry still;
And let the world laugh, an' it will.

Let others muse on earthly things —
The fall of thrones, the fate of kings,
   And those whose fame the world doth fill;
Whilst muffins sit enthroned in trays,
And orange punch in winter sways
The merry sceptre of my days —
   And let the world laugh, an' it will.

Translated by H. W. LONGFELLOW

In the opening couplet and first stanza of this witty poem Góngora expresses his disdain for fame and fortune and his preference for the simple pleasures of life. The opening couplet was a popular saying of the time.

Ande yo caliente

Ande yo caliente,
y ríase la gente.

Traten otros del gobierno
del mundo y sus monarquías,
mientras gobiernan mis días
mantequillas y pan tierno,
y las mañanas de invierno
naranjada y aguardiente,
y ríase la gente.

LUIS DE GÓNGORA

A Powerful Gentleman Is Sir Money!

A powerful gentleman
Is Sir Money!

Mother, I humble myself before money;
He is my lover and my beloved,
And from being so much in love
He always has a golden glow;
And whether a large coin or small,
He does all that I bid him —
A powerful gentleman
Is Sir Money!

Francisco Gómez de Quevedo (1580-1645), Spain's greatest satirist, took an active part in the politics and intrigues of seventeenth-century Madrid. Endowed with a keen mind and brilliant technical skill, the versatile Quevedo cultivated almost all literary genres. His forte, however, is witty satire, best seen in his picaresque novel El buscón, *and in his masterpiece* Los sueños, *a bitter portrayal of the corruption and degeneracy of his day. This is the first stanza of Quevedo's famous poem on the power of money—*Poderoso caballero es don Dinero.

Poderoso caballero es don Dinero

Poderoso caballero
es don Dinero.

Madre, yo al oro me humillo;
él es mi amante y mi amado,
pues de puro enamorado,
de continuo anda amarillo;
que pues, doblón o sencillo,
hace todo cuanto quiero,
poderoso caballero
es don Dinero.

FRANCISCO DE QUEVEDO

Death Warnings

I saw the ramparts of my native land,
One time so strong, now dropping in decay,
Their strength destroyed by this new age's way
That has worn out and rotted what was grand.

I went into the fields; there I could see
The sun drink up the waters newly thawed;
And on the hills the moaning cattle pawed;
Their miseries robbed the light of day for me.

I went into my house; I saw how spotted,
Decaying things made that old home their prize;
My withered walking-staff had come to bend.

I felt the age had won; my sword was rotted;
And there was nothing on which to set my eyes
That was not a reminder of the end.

Translated by JOHN MASEFIELD

Living toward the end of Spain's Golden Age (ca. 1550-1650), Quevedo could sense that decadence and decay would soon befall his country. The powerful sonnet given above may be taken literally as Quevedo's individual reaction to the irresistible ravages of time and death—or more broadly to Spain or perhaps the world as a whole.

Avisos de la muerte

Miré los muros de la patria mía,
si un tiempo fuertes, ya desmoronados,
de la carrera de la edad cansados,
por quien caduca ya su valentía.

Sálima al campo; vi que el sol bebía
los arroyos del hielo desatados,
y del monte quejosos los ganados,
que con sombras hurtó su luz al día.

Entré en mi casa; vi que, amancillada,
de anciana habitación era despojos;
mi báculo, más corvo y menos fuerte.

Vencida de edad sentí mi espada,
y no hallé cosa en que poner los ojos
que no fuese recuerdo de la muerte.

FRANCISCO DE QUEVEDO

Of a sage, who roamed dejected,
Poor and wretched, it is said,
That one day, his wants being fed
By the herbs which he collected,
"Is there one" (he thus reflected)
"Poorer than I am today?"
Turning round him to survey,
He his answer got, detecting
A still poorer sage collecting
Even the leaves he threw away.

Translated by DENIS FLORENCE MacCARTHY

Pedro Calderón de la Barca (1600-1681) was Spain's greatest dramatist during the last years of her literary Golden Age (ca. 1550-1650). Probably the most generally known of Spanish plays is his philosophical drama La vida es sueño (Life Is a Dream). *In this excerpt from the beginning of the play, Rosaura has accidentally entered the tower where Prince Segismundo, who has been held prisoner all his life, is lamenting his fate. To comfort him, she tells this story.*

La vida es sueño

Cuentan de un sabio que un día
tan pobre y mísero estaba,
que sólo se sustentaba
de unas yerbas que cogía.
¿Habrá otro — entre sí decía —
más pobre y triste que yo?
Y cuando el rostro volvió,
halló la respuesta, viendo
que iba otro sabio cogiendo
las hojas que él arrojó.

PEDRO CALDERÓN DE LA BARCA

What Is Life?

What is life? A frenzy.
What is life? An illusion,
A shadow, a fiction,
And the greatest good is small;
For all life is a dream,
And dreams themselves are dreams.

Toward the end of Act II of Life Is a Dream, *Segismundo is returned to his prison, after having been allowed to live as prince for a few hours. He has been persuaded that he has dreamed that experience. Segismundo's famous soliloquy ends with these six lines.*

¿Qué es la vida?

¿Qué es la vida? Un frenesí.
¿Qué es la vida? Una ilusión,
una sombra, una ficción,
y el mayor bien es pequeño;
que toda la vida es sueño,
y los sueños sueños son.

PEDRO CALDERÓN DE LA BARCA

Epigram

A Portuguese was astonished
To see that in their tender childhood
All the young children of France
Could speak French.
"It's black magic,"
He said, twisting his moustache,
"For in order to speak French
A gentleman in Portugal
Reaches old age and speaks it badly,
And here a child speaks it fluently."

Nicolás Fernández de Moratín (1737-1780) was a poet and dramatist. (His fame, incidentally, is eclipsed by that of his more celebrated son, the dramatist Leandro Fernández de Moratín.) The epigram given here is a humorous commentary on the difficulty of learning a foreign language.

Epígrama

Admiróse un portugués
de ver que en su tierna infancia
todos los niños de Francia
supiesen hablar francés.
— Arte diabólica es, —
dijo, torciendo el mostacho,
— pues para hablar en gabacho
un hidalgo en Portugal
llega a viejo y lo habla mal,
y aquí lo parla un muchacho.

NICOLÁS FERNÁNDEZ DE MORATÍN

The Ass and the Flute

This little fable heard,
It good or ill may be;
But it has just occurred
Thus accidentally.

Passing my abode,
Some fields adjoining me
A big Ass on his road
Came accidentally.

And laid upon the spot,
A flute he chanced to see,
A shepherd had forgot
There accidentally.

The animal in front
To scan it nigh came he,
And snuffing loud as wont,
Blew accidentally.

The air it chanced around
The pipe went passing free
And thus the flute a sound
Gave accidentally.

"Oh then," exclaimed the Ass,
"I know to play it fine;
And who for bad shall class
This music asinine?"

El burro flautista

Esta fabulilla,
salga bien o mal,
me ha ocurrido ahora
por casualidad.

Cerca de unos prados
que hay en mi lugar,
pasaba un Borrico
por casualidad.

Una flauta en ellos
halló, que un zagal
se dejó olvidada
por casualidad.

Acercóse a olerla
el dicho animal;
y dió un resoplido
por casualidad.

En la flauta el aire
se hubo de colar;
y sonó la flauta
por casualidad.

"¡Oh!" — dijo el Borrico —
¡Qué bien sé tocar!
¡Y dirán que es mala
la música asnal!"

Without the rules of art,
Even asses, we agree,
May once succeed in part,
Thus accidentally.

Translated by JAMES KENNEDY

Spain's two great writers of fables in verse, Tomás de Iriarte (1750-1791) and Félix María de Samaniego (1745-1801), were contemporaries.

Iriarte's seventy-six fables are contained in his Fábulas literarias (Literary Fables), which contain advice for and criticism of his fellow authors. The Ass and the Flue and The Bear, The Monkey and the Hog, included here, are two of the most popular.

Sin reglas del arte,
borriquitos hay
que una vez aciertan
por casualidad.

TOMÁS DE IRIARTE

ır, with whom a Piedmontese
    ing living made,
    ..ce he had not learned with ease,
On his two feet essayed.

And as he highly of it thought,
He to the Monkey cried,
"How's that?" who, being better taught,
" 'Tis very bad," replied.

"I do believe," rejoined the Bear,
"You little favor show:
For have I not a graceful air,
And step with ease to go?"

A Hog, that was beside them set,
Cried, "Bravo! Good!" said he;
"A better dancer never yet
I saw, and ne'er shall see."

On this the Bear, as if he turned
His thoughts within his mind,
With modest gesture seeming learned
A lesson thence to find.

"When blamed the Monkey, it was cause
Enough for doubting sad;
But when I have the Hog's applause,
It must be very bad!"

As treasured gift, let authors raise
This moral from my verse:
'Tis bad, when wise ones do not praise;
But when fools *do,* 'tis worse.

Translated by JAMES KENNEDY

El oso, la mona y el cerdo

Un Oso, con que la vida
ganaba un piamontés,
la no muy bien aprendida
danza ensayaba en dos pies.

Queriendo hacer de persona,
dijo a una Mona: "¿Qué tal?"
Era perita la Mona,
y respondióle: "Muy mal."

"Yo creo," replicó el Oso,
"que me haces poco favor.
¡Pues qué! ¿Mi aire no es garboso?
¿No hago el paso con primor?"

Estaba el Cerdo presente,
y dijo: "Bravo, ¡bien va!
Bailarín más excelente
no se ha visto ni se verá."

Echó el Oso, al oír esto,
sus cuentas allá entre sí,
y con ademán modesto
hubo de exclamar así:

"Cuando me desaprobaba
la Mona, llegué a dudar;
mas ya que el Cerdo me alaba,
muy mal debo de bailar."

Guarde para su regalo
esta sentencia un autor;
si el sabio no aprueba, ¡malo!
si el necio aplaude, ¡peor!

TOMÁS DE IRIARTE

The Dog and the Crocodile

A dog, while drinking from the Nile,
Was running at the same time.
"Drink without moving about," said to him
A sly crocodile.

The prudent dog said to him:
"It may be harmful to drink and walk,
But is it healthy to wait
Until you sink your teeth in me?"

Oh, what a wise old dog!
I respect your judgment
In this matter of not following
The advice of an enemy.

Félix María de Samaniego (1745-1801) is Iriarte's rival as Spain's leading fabulist. Many of Samaniego's Fábulas morales (Moral Fables) are familiar to us, since he often imitated popular French and Greek authors, like La Fontaine and Aesop.

El perro y el cocodrilo

Bebiendo un perro en el Nilo,
al mismo tiempo corría.
— Bebe quieto — le decía
un taimado cocodrilo.

Díjole el perro prudente:
— Dañoso es beber y andar,
pero ¿es sano el aguardar
a que me claves el diente?

¡Oh, qué docto perro viejo!
Yo venero tu sentir
en esto de no seguir
del enemigo el consejo.

FÉLIX MARÍA DE SAMANIEGO

The Hen That Laid the Golden Eggs

There once was a hen that laid
A golden egg for its owner each day.
Not satisfied even with such profit,
The avaricious rich man wanted
To discover once and for all the gold mine,
And to find in less time more treasure.
He killed it, he opened its stomach immediately,
But after examining it,
What happened? That, since the hen was dead,
He lost his golden egg and didn't find a mine.

How many there are who, having enough,
Wish to become rich instantly,
Undertaking projects
At times with such rapid consequences,
That in only a few months,
When they already see themselves as marquises
Counting their millions,
Find themselves in the street without a pair of pants!

La gallina de los huevos de oro

Érase una Gallina que ponía
un huevo de oro al dueño cada día.
Aun con tanta ganancia mal contento,
quiso el rico avariento
descubrir de una vez la mina de oro,
y hallar en menos tiempo más tesoro.
Matóla, abrióle el vientre de contado,
pero después de haberla registrado,
¿qué sucedió?: que, muerta la Gallina,
perdió su huevo de oro y no halló mina.

¡Cuántos hay que teniendo lo bastante,
enriquecerse quieren al instante,
abrazando proyectos
a veces de tan rápidos efectos,
que sólo en pocos meses,
cuando se contemplaban ya marqueses
contando sus millones,
se vieron en la calle sin calzones!

FÉLIX MARÍA DE SAMANIEGO

The Young Philosopher and His Friends

A gentleman young and carefully reared
By a venerable scholar of learning,
Abandoned the books which he long revered —
For the taste of the world he was yearning.
He found himself soon with light company
In whose manner and charm he delighted.
He joined in their quests for gay revelry
And to dine with them soon was invited.
But when he arrived with gay comraderie
To sup at the table's sweet savors,
— Unspeakable horrors! Brute savagery! —
The table was full of cadavers;
"You eat unashamed these spoils of death?"
Declaimed the young man with a sigh.

The guests, looking up without catching breath,
Whilst devouring a bird, did reply:
"If you want to live with us happily,
Our manners and customs you will follow."
So saying, they passed to him graciously
A bird they implored him to swallow.
"That may be so, what you have just said;
Remorse your reflections instill.
But after all, it's already dead,
And if you don't eat it, we will."

El joven filósofo y sus compañeros

Un joven, educado
con el mayor cuidado
por un viejo filósofo profundo,
salió por fin a visitar el mundo.
Concurrió cierto día
entre civil y alegre compañía
a una mesa abundante y primorosa.
—¡Espectáculo horrendo! ¡Fiera cosa!
¡La mesa de cadáveres cubierta
a la vista del hombre! . . . ¡Y éste acierta
a comer los despojos de la muerte! —
el joven declamaba de esta suerte.

Al son de filosóficas razones,
devorando perdices y pichones,
le responden algunos concurrentes:
— Si usted ha de vivir entre las gentes,
deberá hacerse a todo. —
Con un gracioso modo,
alabando el bocado de exquisito,
le presentan un gordo pajarito.
— Cuanto usted ha exclamado, será cierto;
mas en fin, le decían, ya está muerto.
Pruébelo por su vida . . . Considere
que otro lo comerá, si no lo quiere. —

Looking on those who partook with delight
Of the food in this sumptuous feast,
And breathing the scent of the birds did excite
In the young man a lust for the beast.
"Who could have said that me, too, they would find
Eating an innocent creature!"
But still he ate on, not seeming to mind
His own philosophic forfeiture.
Once having fallen, he fell once again;
From his early maxims he did stray.
From quail to woodcock he went without strain,
Like a wild beast devouring his prey.

In this way we may see how bad habits creep in,
And our hearts from good ways they sever.
Enslaved we become and continue to sin,
Their whims we must follow forever.
So rash never be in deed or in word —
Take heed and beware: resist the first bird!

Translated by Lillian Resnick

La ocasión, las palabras, el ejemplo,
y según yo contemplo,
yo no sé qué olorcillo
que exhalaba el caliente pajarillo,
al joven persuadieron de manera
que al fin se lo comió: — ¡Quién lo dijera!
¡Haber yo devorado un inocente! —
Así clamaba, pero fríamente.
Lo cierto es que, llevado de aquel cebo,
con más facilidad cayó de nuevo;
la ocasión se repite
de uno en otro convite,
y de una codorniz a una becada,
llegó el joven al fin de la jornada,
olvidando sus máximas primeras,
a ser devorador como las fieras.

De esta suerte los vicios se insinúan,
crecen, se perpetúan
dentro del corazón de los humanos
hasta ser sus señores y tiranos.
Pues, ¿qué remedio? . . . Incautos jovencitos,
¡cuenta con los primeros pajaritos!

FÉLIX MARÍA DE SAMANIEGO

Sail on, swift bark, at my command,
So brave and bold,
No warship by your foeman manned,
Nor storm, nor calm, nor any force
Shall turn you from your chosen course
Nor daunt your hardy soul.

A score of ships
We've seized aright
And this despite
The English fleet.
And I have forced
A hundred lords
To lay their swords
Beneath my feet.

My only treasure a pirate ship,
My god but liberty,
My law, brute force and hearty wind,
My land, the open sea.

Translated by ALICE JANE McVAN

José de Espronceda (1808-1842), the outstanding lyric poet of the romantic period, himself exemplified the spirit of romanticism in his stormy life. His favorite themes in many of his poems are the unfortunates and the outcasts of our society—the pirate, the beggar, the executioner. The musical quality of Espronceda is especially evident in these stanzas from his Canción del pirata.

Canción del pirata

— Navega, velero mío,
sin temor;
que ni enemigo navío,
ni tormenta, ni bonanza,
tu rumbo a torcer alcanza,
ni a sujetar tu valor.

Veinte presas
hemos hecho
a despecho
del inglés,
y han rendido
cien naciones
sus pendones
a mis pies.

Que es mi barco mi tesoro,
que es mi Dios la libertad,
mi ley, la fuerza y el viento,
mi única patria, la mar.

JOSÉ DE ESPRONCEDA

Upon hearing a man speak, it is easy
To guess where he was born:
If he praises England, he is probably an Englishman;
If he speaks ill of Germany, he is a Frenchman;
And if he speaks ill of Spain, he is a Spaniard.

This redondilla *(five-line poem) by the Catalan poet Joaquín María Bartrina (1850-1880) humorously points up the individuality of the Spanish people. A Spaniard is his own severest critic.*

Arabesco

Oyendo hablar a un hombre, fácil es
acertar donde vió la luz del sol:
si os alaba a Inglaterra, será inglés;
si os habla mal de Prusia, es un francés;
y si habla mal de España, es español.

JOAQUÍN MARÍA BARTRINA

In this treacherous world,
Nothing is completely true or completely false;
Everything depends upon the color
Of the glasses that you use.

Ramón de Campoamor (1817-1901) achieved great popularity in his own day with his short poems expressing semi-philosophical wisdom. The stanza above comes from Las dos linternas (The Two Lanterns), *a poem about the search for truth.*

En el mundo traidor

Y es que en el mundo traidor
nada hay verdad ni mentira;
todo es según el color
del cristal con que se mira.

RAMÓN DE CAMPOAMOR

Rima VII

In a dark corner of the parlor,
Perhaps forgotten by its owner,
Silent and covered with dust,
The harp was seen.

How many notes slumbered in its strings —
Just as a bird sleeps in the branches —
Waiting for the snow-white hand
That can pluck them!

Alas, I thought, how many times does genius
Sleep like this in the depths of the soul
And, like Lazarus, waits for a voice
To bid it: "Arise and walk!"

The seventy-six short rimas of Gustavo Adolfo Bécquer (1836-1870) have won for their author the first place among the Spanish poets of the nineteenth century. These delicate, bitter-sweet love poems are based in part upon his own unhappy life.

Rima VII

Del salón en el ángulo obscuro,
de su dueño tal vez olvidada,
silenciosa y cubierta de polvo
    veíase el arpa.

¡Cuánta nota dormía en sus cuerdas,
como el pájaro duerme en las ramas,
esperando la mano de nieve
    que sabe arrancarlas!

¡Ay! pensé, ¡cuántas veces el genio
así duerme en el fondo del alma
y una voz, como Lázaro, espera
    que le diga: "Levántate y anda!"

GUSTAVO ADOLFO BÉCQUER

"I am ardent, I am dark-skinned,
I am the symbol of passion;
My soul yearns for pleasures.
Is it me that you seek?" "No, not thee."

"My brow is pale, my hair is golden,
I can offer you joy without end;
I have a treasure house of tenderness.
Is it me that you seek?" "No, not thee."

"I am a dream, an impossible
Vague phantom of mist and light;
I am without body, I am intangible;
I cannot love you." "Oh, come, come thou!"

Rima XI

— Yo soy ardiente, yo soy morena,
yo soy el símbolo de la pasión;
de ansia de goces mi alma está llena.
¿A mí me buscas? — No es a ti, no.

— Mi frente es pálida; mis trenzas de oro;
puedo brindarte dichas sin fin;
yo de ternura guardo un tesoro.
¿A mí me llamas? — No es a ti, no.

— Yo soy un sueño, un imposible
vano fantasma de niebla y luz;
soy incorpórea, soy intangible;
no puedo amarte. — ¡Oh, ven; ven tú!

GUSTAVO ADOLFO BÉCQUER

Rima XXI

> "What is poetry?" you say as you fix
> Upon my eyes your eyes of blue.
> What is poetry? And you ask me that?
> Poetry . . . is you!

Rima XX

¿Qué es poesía? dices mientras clavas
en mi pupila tu pupila azul;
¿Qué es poesía? ¿Y tú me lo preguntas?
Poesía . . . eres tú.

GUSTAVO ADOLFO BÉCQUER

Cordoba.
Distant and lonely.

Black my pony, full the moon,
And olives stowed in my saddle-bags.
Though well I may know the way
I'll never arrive at Cordoba.

Across the plain, through the wind,
Black my pony, red the moon.
Stark death is staring at me
From the tall towers of Cordoba.

Alas, how long is the way!
Alas, for my brave black pony!
Alas, stark death awaits me
Before I arrive at Cordoba!

Cordoba.
Distant and lonely.

Translated by ELEANOR L. TURNBULL

Undoubtedly the most popular Spanish writer of this century was the gifted Federico García Lorca (1898-1936), who met a tragic death at the outbreak of the Spanish civil war. As poet and dramatist, Lorca has achieved a lasting reputation at home and abroad. Lorca often sought inspiration in the traditions and folk songs of his native Andalusia.

Canción de jinete

Córdoba.
Lejana y sola.

Jaca negra, luna grande,
y aceitunas en mi alforja.
Aunque sepa los caminos
yo nunca llegaré a Córdoba.

Por el llano, por el viento,
jaca negra, luna roja.
La muerte me está mirando
desde las torres de Córdoba.

¡Ay, qué camino tan largo!
¡Ay, mi jaca valerosa!
¡Ay, que la muerte me espera
antes de llegar a Córdoba!

Córdoba.
Lejana y sola.

FEDERICO GARCÍA LORCA

Index